ALSO BY CRIS EVATT

Café Conversations
Stop Arguing with Reality
Simply Organized!
30 Days to a Simpler Life
The Givers & the Takers

The
Myth
of
Free Will

Edited by Cris Evatt

Café Essays
PRINCEVILLE, HI

Café Essays

PRINCEVILLE, HI

CafeEssays@crisevatt.com

Book Design: Caroline Culver
Cover Art: Debbie Morris
Editorial Suggestions: Anne DeCamp

ISBN 978-0-9708181-7-1

Psychology/Self-Help/Science

First Café Essays Edition: 2007

To Ramesh S. Balsekar

Contents

Foreword

*D*oes everyone wonder about Free Will? Certainly the world's great thinkers have struggled with the problem, as have the scientists, philosophers and psychologists gathered together in this delightful collection. Indeed Free Will is said to be the most discussed philosophical problem ever. But it's not a problem we should leave to philosophers, for it concerns us all, tangling as it does with issues of morality, wisdom and the meaning of life.

In fact I suspect that at some level everyone who thinks at all must have asked themselves questions such as Who am I? Why do I end up doing things I didn't want to do? Is everything inevitable, and if so why should I bother doing anything at all?

To my surprise I recently discovered that even my Dad does.

My father is not an educated man. He left school at fifteen, fought in the Second World War, came home to take over his father's printing business and, as far as I know, never read a book the rest of his life. He did not share my mother's strong Christian faith, which provoked endless arguments between her and me, nor did he enjoy discussing life, the universe and everything. Looking back I see him as a straightforward, honest and kindly man, a father I could admire, but not one I could share my ideas with—not someone I thought would have anything to say about Free Will. But I was wrong, as I learned one evening, having a drink by the fire with him before I set off to give an evening lecture.

"Where did you say you were going dear?" he asked for the third or fourth time.

"To Sharpham House. It's a Buddhist center near Totnes."

"Why are you going there?"

"I'm giving a lecture on Free Will."

"Free Will? What is there to say about that?"

How do you explain the problem of Free Will to a man of ninety who has advanced dementia, just about knows who you are, and whose world consists of not much more than a bed, a fireside chair, and the daily paper he can no longer understand?

I did my best. I said that it seemed to me that my body and brain are clever machines that can function perfectly well without there being any inner me, or spirit or soul, to direct them. So there's a problem —I seem to be in control but I cannot really be. This is, I said, what I was going to be talking about.

To my complete surprise this set him alight. He

was quite sure that he had, or was, such an inner spirit; it stood to reason, he had to be. I asked him where this spirit came from, and he said from God. I protested that there was no God, and that spirits controlling a body would have to be magic, and he came back with a comment I have never forgotten.

"If there is no spirit, then why do we want to be good?"

He didn't ask why we are good, or argue about good and evil, he simply asked, "Why do we *want* to be good".

This struck me so hard because I, too, have come to this point in my own, very different, struggles. I have long assumed that Free Will is an illusion and have worked hard to live without it, but doing this provokes a simple fear—what if I behave terribly badly? What if I give up all moral values and do terrible things? What indeed are moral values and how can I make moral decisions if there's no one inside who is responsible? I'm sure I don't need to go on. I suspect that this natural fear is the main reason why so few people sincerely try to live without Free Will. Like my Dad, they want to be good, and fear that if they stop believing in a self who chooses to do the right thing then they will run amok and all hell will break loose.

Is the fear justified? I suspect not. Evolutionary psychology provides reasons why we want to be good, such as nurturing instincts shaped by kin selection, and the desire to earn brownie points in the game of reciprocal altruism; memetics provides other reasons, showing how altruistic *memes* (units of cultural information transferrable from one mind to another) can spread so successfully; and most of us have been trained since early childhood to behave at least reasonably decently. So it may just come naturally to us to want to be good, even though we so often fail. If this is true, this common fear is no excuse to carry on living in delusion.

Arguably, some of our most cruel and selfish behaviour is caused, or at least exacerbated, by clinging to a false sense of an inner self who has consciousness and Free Will, in which case we might even behave better, rather than worse, if we could throw off the illusion. So it is by no means obvious that giving up believing in Free Will must be morally dangerous.

Another deep seated fear is that we will fail to do anything at all, and lose all motivation. I have frequently had students who thought this way, "Why would I ever get up in the morning?" they ask. I suggest they try the exercise and see what happens.

What happens is that they lie there and get bored. Then they need to go to the loo, and once in the bathroom it seems nicer to have a shower and clean their teeth than go back to bed. Then they get hungry. And so the day goes on and things get done. In fact, if you keep practicing this way it becomes increasingly obvious that the physical body you once thought you inhabited does not need a driver or a ghostly supervisor. Distributed through its multiple parallel systems are the instincts, memories, control systems and skills of a lifetime that will ensure its coordinated actions and appropriate responses. It really is okay to trust in the universe and in one's own spontaneous actions. Then the feeling of Free Will simply loses its power.

My Dad stopped at his question about goodness. Many people cannot accept his answer and want to go further. But in my experience—and I've asked many scientists and philosophers, as well as my own students—most *intellectually* reject the reality of Free Will while carrying on their lives "as if" it exists. Indeed, I have often been told that it's impossible to live one's life without the illusion, and that everyone who lives happily and sanely must live "as if" they are free.

Whether you agree with them or not, you will find this little book packed with exciting and challenging thoughts on Free Will, from some of the greatest minds of our time. Read it right through, or dip into it when you feel the illusion of Free Will creeping over you, and I'm sure you'll enjoy it as much as I have.

—Susan Blackmore, Ph.D.

Introduction

Most people believe that Free Will exists. They experience it and feel it. They're certain they have Free Will. *This book asks you to think less like most people.* It asks you to learn why Free Will is a myth, a belief, and a story. It asks you to learn more about your amazing brain.

Four years ago, I was introduced to the ideas of Ramesh Balsekar, an Advaita (non-duality) master who lives in Mumbai and gives daily talks, *satsangs*. "You are not the doer," he tells his visitors. "Each human being is a uniquely programmed organism whose programming is its genes and ongoing conditioning. Ramana Maharshi, Nisargadatta Maharaj and Buddha taught the same thing."

Still, I was skeptical. I wondered, what do the world's leading scientists and other prominent thinkers have to say about Free Will? Do they agree with these gurus?

Next, I went on a research binge. I googled "Free Will" and up popped several fascinating websites with chats, books, and articles. I studied them all and found many more as time passed. I sought opinions "for" and "against" Free Will, but found no credible evidence for it.

I did, however, find a lively debate: Some scholars argue that we should keep the Free Will illusion around because dropping it threatens moral responsibility (and might freak some people out). The majority disagree and believe we can live happily with the unadorned facts. "Let's tough it out, be gutsy, progressive." Perhaps, you'll have an opinion on this matter later on.

The essays in this anthology feature the *crème de la crème* of my research and were written after the year 2000, so you will be reading current opinions. As you read them, notice how often the authors make similar points. Don't let this stop you from appreciating all of the essays.

The Four Realizations introduce the concepts and terminology in the essays. I capitalized "free will" to make it stand out on a page. Capitals were not used in the original sources.

And while you are reading, ask yourself, "Who would I be without my belief in Free Will?"

—Cris Evatt

The
Four
Realizations

When things turn out well,
we say we have Free Will.
When they turn out badly,
we say it's our destiny.

REALIZATION 1

"I choose, therefore I have Free Will."
Is that true?

Choosing is a very real human experience. The brain's decision-making circuitry, in the frontal lobes, controls our choices. When we choose between a papaya and a banana, patterns of neural activity representing these two possibilities appear in the cortex. Copies of each pattern grow and spread at different rates, depending on the our experiences and sensory impressions. Eventually, the number of copies of one pattern passes a threshold, and we pick the papaya or the banana.

"Decision making is a competition, a dynamic process in which there are winners and losers. The losers are never eliminated, but stick around to try and win again," writes Alain Berthoz in *Emotion & Reason*. Suppressed actions are always poised for a comeback.

Decision making is an extremely complex behavior. Our brains store millions of emotional memories of past decisions, and these memories drive our choices. The choices that bring the most pleasure (and often, the least pain) win because the brain favors the path of least resistance.

REALIZATION 2

Our genes and conditioning produce our choices.

Our behavior is determined by our heredity (genes) and environment (conditioning) and their complex interaction in the brain. Encoded in our DNA is our race, sex, personality, and appearance. Our conditioning includes what we learn from our parents, schooling, culture, social status, generation, and historical time-slot.

"At any given moment, unfolding inside of each person, there is a complex genetic and environmental legacy, which at times can have a massive unforeseen impact upon our lives," says Arnell Dowret, radio producer. "As this is happening, we are also interacting with a changing environment." New determinants are constantly being factored into our lives. Some are minor, such as needing a new light bulb, or catching a cold, and some are major, such as breaking a leg, meeting one's future spouse, or receiving a huge inheritance.

Accepting that our choices and actions are determined by our genes and conditioning does not diminish our capacity to change and grow.

REALIZATION 3

Free Will is a myth
about supernatural powers.

The Free Will myth says that humans are imbued with a "spirit" or "soul" or "some magical quality" that directs the brain's decision-making circuitry. This ghostly, free-floating, supernatural agent can override our genes and conditioning.

But how does a nonphysical spirit communicate with a physical body part? And how does it control decision-making? People who believe in Free Will avoid these questions. Below is an excerpt from Scott Adams's book *God's Debris*.

"So where is Free Will?" he asked again.

"It must involve the soul." I didn't have a better answer.

"Soul? Where is the soul located?"

"It's not located anywhere. It just is."

"Then the soul is not physical in nature, according to you," he said.

"I guess not. Otherwise someone probably would have found physical evidence of it," I said.

"So you believe that the soul, which is *not* physical, can influence the brain, which is physical?"

REALIZATION 4
Everything that happens has a *cause*.

"Determinism" is the view that all events, including human thoughts and actions, are caused by an unbroken chain of prior occurrences. No utterly random events can occur. Causality rules. Therefore, no immaterial "spirit" or "soul" or "magical quality" can override the brain and control decision making. Such an entity would be unnecessary. Nature is all that is needed, and nothing can exist apart from it. The universe cannot be divided into "natural" and "supernatural."

Happily, determinism is *not* the same as fatalism, the harsh, depressing concept that says our every move is mapped out. Behavior is never perfectly predictable or inevitable. It's quirky.

The realization that our behavior is produced by *causes*—our genes and conditioning—enables us takes ourselves and others less seriously. It leads to less pride and blame.

As you read, pay special attention to these words: causes, causation, causality, contra-causal, causal chains/stories, determined, determinants, and determinism.

The Essays

*I believe that science gives us
the deepest possible sense of grandeur
and wonder about our place
in time and space.*

—MICHAEL SHERMER

Demystifying the Illusion

by Daniel M. Wegner

Daniel Wegner is a professor of psychology at Harvard University.

So, here you are reading a book on Free Will. How could this have happened? One way to explain it would be to examine the *causes* of your behavior.

A team of scientific psychologists could study your reported thoughts, emotions, and motives, your genetics and your history of learning, your social situation and culture, your memories, physiology and neuroanatomy, and lots of other things. If they had access to all of the data they could ever want, the assumption of psychology is that they could uncover the mechanism that gives rise to all your behavior and so could explain why you picked up this book at this moment.

However, another way to explain the fact of your reading this book is to say you decided to pick it up and begin reading. You freely willed what you are doing. You have a kind of personal power, an ability to do what you want when you want.

These two explanations are both appealing but in different ways. The scientific explanation accounts for behavior as a machine and appeals to that part of us that knows how useful science is for understanding the world. It would be wonderful if we could understand people in just the same way.

The Free Will explanation has a much deeper grip on our intuition. It feels more right.

Why? Because we each experience ourselves willing our actions many times a day.

We feel that we cause ourselves to behave.

The idea of Free Will and the idea of a psychological mechanism has an oil and water relationship, having never been properly reconciled. One way to put them together is to say that the mechanistic approach is the explanation that is preferred for scientific purposes, but a person's experience of Free Will must be understood scientifically as well.

The mechanisms underlying the experience of will are themselves a topic for study. We should be able to examine and understand what creates the experience of will and what makes it go away.

This means, though, that Free Will is an illusion. It is an illusion in the sense that *the experience of consciously willing an action is not a direct indication that the conscious thought has caused the action.*

POINTS TO PONDER

• Sometimes how things seem is more important than what they are. This is true in theater, in art, in used car sales, in economics, and—it now turns out—in the scientific analysis of Free Will. It seems we have minds. It seems we are free agents. It seems we cause what we do. Although it is sobering and ultimately accurate to call all this an illusion, *it is a mistake to conclude that the illusory is trivial.*

• We experience a walk in the park, winding a clock, or smiling at someone, and the feeling keeps our notions of ourselves as persons intact. But our sense of being a free agent who does things comes at a cost of being technically wrong all of the time. The feeling of doing is how it seems, not what is—but that is as it should be. All is well because *the illusion makes us human.*

TO GO DEEPER

• For Daniel Wegner, our experience of Free Will is a "feeling" that is similar to the way happiness and sadness are feelings. Read his new book: *The Illusion of Conscious Will.*

• His website: www.wjh.harvard.edu/~wegner

Cartoon by Don Addis

Choosing Chocolate

by Laurence Tancredi

Laurence Tancredi, a psychiatrist-lawyer, is a Clinical Professor of Psychiatry at New York University School of Medicine.

We go into an ice cream parlor and choose chocolate over vanilla. It is a seemingly simply choice, and we claim that our taste preference has dictated it. Yet choices are never that simple.

The choice of chocolate ice cream is influenced not only by taste, but also by color, texture, presentation—and more than likely by earlier pleasant memories associated with flavor.

Nonetheless the decision about ice cream is simple compared to decisions about which strategy to select to solve a complex math problem, or to personal choices like whether to leave one's job for one that pays less but might provide more opportunity for advancement—or for one that is more fulfilling though is might pay less and offer little opportunity for advancement.

Choices of any complexity always involve layers of multifaceted mental activity, and often many interrelated decisions.

But neuroscience is forcing us to rethink the extent of our personal control over our choices, and the implications of the limits on personal control over our choices are nothing short of mind-boggling. Imagine that Free Will, long regarded as a hallmark of the human condition, may not be an untrammeled quality.

Imagine that we are not quite as "free" as we would wish—and that biological forces produced by genes and the environment may be more powerful than anyone every believed possible in influencing an individual's decisions.

POINTS TO PONDER
• It seems that the more complex the choice, the more we are fortified in our conviction of ownership, autonomy, and self-determination.
• Social morality begins in the brain, for without the brain, there would be no concept of morality.

TO GO DEEPER
Read Laurence Tancredi's provocative new bestseller *Hardwired Behavior: What Neuroscience Reveals about Morality*. He updates the debate between biology and blameworthiness.

Feeling Free

by Michael Shermer

Michael Shermer is the founding publisher of Skeptic magazine and a columnist for Scientific American.

Scholars of considerable intellectual power for many millennia have failed to resolve the paradox of feeling free in a determined universe. One provisional solution is to think of the universe as so complex that the number of causes and the complexity of their interactions make the predetermination of human action pragmatically impossible. We can even put a figure on the causal net of the universe to see just how absurd it is to think we can get our minds around it fully.

It has been computed that in order for a computer in the far future of the universe to resurrect in a virtual reality every person who ever lived or could have lived, with all causal interactions between themselves and their environment, it would need 10 to the power of 10 to the power of 123 bits (a 1 followed by 10^{123} zeros) of memory. Suffice it to say that no computer within the conceivable future will achieve this level of power; likewise no human brain even comes close.

The enormity of this complexity leads us to feel as if we are acting freely as uncaused causers, even though we are actually causally determined. Since no set of causes we select as the determiners of human action can be complete, *the feeling of freedom arises out of this ignorance of causes.* To that extent we may act as if we are free. There is much to gain, little to lose, and personal responsibility follows.

TO GO DEEPER
• Read Michael Shermer's fascinating and well-researched books: *Why People Believe Weird Things, Science Friction,* and *Why Darwin Matters: The Case Against Intelligent Design.* He debunks superstitions and ignorance about science.
• Join "The Skeptics Society" and subscribe to *Skeptic* magazine at www.skeptic.com.
• His motto: "Cognite tute—think for yourself."

Causally Bound

by Arnell Dowret

Dowret is a freethought activist, writer, and associate producer-host of WBAI radio program "Equal Time for Freethought" in New York City.

Our universe appears to be governed by the laws of cause-and-effect and human behavior is no exception to this rule.

For most people, however, the mere suggestion that human behavior is the result of causes, and is not the result of choice, often results in them putting up a wall that greatly reduces their abilities to hear anything further on the subject.

The idea that human behavior is forced and not chosen seems to contradict and undermine the ways in which we experience ourselves and the ways in which we have learned to regard the behavior of others.

Despite this, there exists no legitimate evidence for anything that can account for the way that we behave other than the complex combination of our genes and the way in which they interact with our environment.

Our actions should be based
on the ever-present awareness
that human beings in their
thinking, feeling, and acting
are not free, but are just as
causally bound as the stars
in their motion.

—ALBERT EINSTEIN

The Princeton Survey

by Lee M. Silver

Lee Silver holds a Ph.D. in Biophysics from Harvard University and is a professor of Molecular Biology at Princeton University.

The conviction that human beings are endowed with Free Will is pervasive, even more so than a belief in the human soul. In my anonymous survey of 335 randomly chosen undergraduates at Princeton, 78 percent expressed confidence in the existence of Free Will, while only 53 percent were confident about an immaterial human spirit. (Students could answer "yes," "no," and "I am not sure what I think.")

Most dramatic was the difference in responses from male and female students. Of the 173 women surveyed, only three (compared with 19 out of 162 men) were confident enough in their personal convictions to answer "no" to the existence of Free Will.

A spirit or soul are terms for an imagined physical entity that controls physical objects. According to Owen Flanagan, a philosopher and popular author, a belief in Free Will serves as a "quick and reliable diagnostic test" for an implicit belief in some kind of soul because "the only device ever invented that can do this sort of job (expressing Free Will) is an incorporeal soul or spirit." And yet remarkably, a quarter of the students at Princeton have faith in Free Will at the same time they claim to reject the existence of immaterial human spirits.

POINTS TO PONDER

• Why should we believe that God created regions of the brain to receive his communications instead of the converse idea that human brains are wired to create an illusion of higher spirits or God?

• As a philosophical concept, Free Will is like an onion whose skin has been completely peeled away: at its core, it ceases to exist.

TO GO DEEPER

Read Lee Silver's new book, *Challenging Nature: The Clash of Science and Spirituality at the New Frontiers of Life*. A provocative look at the collision of science, religion, pseudoscience, and politics.

Delving into the Myth

by William B. Provine

William Provine is a professor at the Cornell University, Department of Ecology and Evolutionary Biology.

*F*rom the perspective of evolutionary biology, organisms are locally *determined* by heredity and environment, and their interaction. Thus no organism can have Free Will, and indeed the idea of Free Will is unintelligible. Humans, however, widely believe in a myth of Free Will.

The question is, do we benefit enough from this myth to justify basing our lives on it? Is the usual philosophical dictum that belief in "free agency" is required for moral responsibility answer enough? Without moral responsibility, societies become bestial and individuals are overcome by nihilism and disillusionment. So say the philosophers.

Does the myth of Free Will have negative social consequences? Yes, and they are huge.

Blame, revenge, and retribution dominate modern society, from personal relationships to between countries.

Evil consequences so outweigh the benefits of belief in the myth of Free Will that, even if we really did have it, *we should pretend we don't.*

I have concluded that Free Will is entirely disconnected from moral responsibility. When an individual behaves well in society, she exhibits her past experiences, education, and training, but no Free Will. Humans can live well without Free Will, and escape entirely nihilism and disillusionment. Human society free of this myth would be kinder and more caring than our present societies.

Using Free Will as an excuse we condone a vicious attitude of revenge toward anyone who does wrong in our society. Most of the movies in the a video store are based upon getting even with some nasty person.

This attitude leads to a grossly expensive and hopeless systems of punishment in America, though much of the same attitude can be found in most countries around the world.

Without the Free Will myth, justification for revenge disappears and rehabilitation becomes the main job of judicial systems and prisons.

We will all live in a better society when this myth is dispelled.

"Where there are two desires
in a man's heart, he has no choice
between the two, but must obey
the strongest, there being no such thing
as Free Will in the composition
of any human being that ever lived."

—**Mark Twain** in *Eruption*

POINTS TO PONDER

• Since the great majority of people on earth believe they have Free Will, and consider it important, would an understanding that they actually had no Free Will at all be a major blow?

• The vast majority of persons experience a 'feeling' of Free Will when making a choice, like choosing vanilla ice cream over chocolate. For them, making choices proves a person has Free Will. No proof could be more obvious. But are choices ever completely free? That question we can answer easily: All human choices are constrained by many *causes*.

• What a relief to me to discover that humans have no such thing as Free Will. I agree 100 percent with Einstein about the benefits of having no Free Will. If someone insists on blaming me, then I diminish the relationship to a manageable level instead of worrying about getting even.

MORE TO EXPLORE

Read another Provine essay on Free Will online: Http://eeb.bio.utk.edu/darwin/DarwinDayProvine Address.htm

Who's to Blame?

by Ramesh S. Balsekar

A commerce graduate from the University of London, Ramesh S. Balsekar was the president of a leading bank in India. Around the world, he is considered a master of pure Advaita.

If one were to choose one single event in our daily living that is the most common, it would perhaps be the fact that in almost any group of people, the subject of the conversation is about someone being blamed—someone is responsible, someone should be punished.

"Blaming" has become the very basis of living and has been causing the suffering which the Buddha considered the essence of life. He therefore concluded that the only way to end this suffering to accept that "Events happen, deeds are done, but there is not individual doer thereof."

The arising of a thought is spontaneous. Anything, of course, can happen, but a thought which is likely to occur to a doctor is not likely to occur to a lawyer or a mechanic. The thought which occurs in a particular organism (human) has to do with its natural characteristics. The thought about the equation which arose in Einstein's brain could not have occurred in anyone else.

Each individual organism is created with certain characteristics, so that certain actions will take place. These actions are part of the impersonal functioning of Totality.

POINTS TO PONDER

The ego of the *sage* (an enlightened person) is totally free from the burden of pride and arrogance for his good actions and guilt and blame for his bad actions, whereas the ego of the ordinary person carries the burden of guilt and shame for his own actions and a heavier burden of hatred for others, for their actions which have hurt him.

TO GO DEEPER

Ramesh Balsekar has written over 20 books which may be purchased from RameshBalsekar.com, Advaita.org and Amazon.com. He elaborates his own concepts with those of his guru Nisargadatta Maharaj, the Buddha, Ramana Maharshi, as well as the teachings of Taoist Masters and Wei Wui Wei.

Freedom Evolves

by Daniel C. Dennett

Dennett studied philosophy at Harvard University and Oxford University. He is now the Austin B. Fletcher Professor of Philosophy and Director of the Center for Cognitive Studies at Tufts University.

*T*he *idea* that we have Free Will is a background condition for our whole way of thinking about our lives. We count on it. We count on people "having Free Will," the same way we count on them falling when pushed off cliffs and needing food and water to live. Free Will is like the air we breathe, and it is present almost everywhere we want to go, but it is not only not eternal, it evolved, and is still evolving.

The atmosphere of our planet evolved over hundreds of millions of years as a product of the activities of simple early life-forms, and it continues to evolve today in response to the activities of the billions of more complex life-forms it made possible. The atmosphere of Free Will is the enveloping, enabling, life-shaping, *conceptual* atmosphere of intentional action: planning, hoping, promising, honoring, blaming, resenting, and punishing.

We all grow up in this *conceptual* atmosphere, and we learn to conduct our lives in the terms that it provides. It *appears to be* as stable, as eternal and unchanging as arithmetic, but it is not.

The idea that we have Free Will evolved as a recent product of human interactions, and some of the kinds of human activity it first made possible on this planet may also threaten to disrupt its future stability, or even hasten its demise. Our planet's atmosphere is not guaranteed to last forever, and neither is our concept of Free Will.

POINTS TO PONDER

• We have more freedom if Determinism is true than if it isn't. Because if Determinism is true, then *there is less randomness*. There's less unpredictability. To have freedom, you need the capacity to make reliable judgments about what's going to happen next, so you can base your actions on it.

• Free Will is not what tradition declares it to be: a God-like power to exempt oneself from the casual fabric of the physical world. It is an evolved creation of human activity and beliefs, and it is just as real as such other human creations as music and money.

• One widespread tradition has it that we human beings are responsible agents, captains of our fate,

27

because what we really are are *souls*, immaterial and immortal clumps of Godstuff that inhabit and control our material bodies rather like spectral puppeteers. It is our souls that are the source of all meaning and the locus of all our suffering, our joy, our glory and shame. But this idea of material souls, capable of defying the laws of physics, has outlived its credibility thanks to the advance of natural sciences.

TO GO DEEPER

Daniel Dennett is best known for his arguments that Free Will boils down to physical processes.

• Read *Freedom Evolves*, especially Chapter Three, "Thinking about Determinism."

• In his latest book, *Breaking the Spell*, Dennett urges readers to examine religion as a product of evolution rather than as a transcendental force.

• Go to www.Skeptic.com to order DVD lectures featuring Dennett.

• His website: http://ase.tufts.edu/cogstud/~ddennett.htm

The Ghost in the Machine

by Steven Pinker

Steven Pinker is a Professor of Psychology at Harvard University having previously been the director of the Center for Cognitive Neuroscience at MIT. He studies the nature of intelligence and workings of the mind.

In the traditional view of "The Ghost in the Machine," our bodies are inhabited by a *self* or *soul* that chooses the behavior to be executed by the body. These choices are not compelled by some prior physical event, like one billiard ball smacking into another and sending it into a corner pocket.

The idea that our behavior is caused by the physiological activity of a genetically-shaped brain refutes the traditional view. It makes our behavior an automatic consequence of molecules in motion and leaves no room for an uncaused chooser.

One fear of determinism is a gaping existential anxiety: that deep down we are not in control of our own choices. All of our brooding and agonizing over the right things to do is pointless, it would seem, because everything has already been preordained by the state of our brains.

If you suffer from this anxiety, I suggest the following experiment: For the next two days, don't bother deliberating over your actions. It's a waste of time; they have already been determined. Shoot from the hip, live for the moment, and if it feels good do it. No, I am not seriously suggesting that you try this! But a moment's reflection on what would happen *if you did* try to give up making decisions should serve as a Valium for your anxiety.

The experience of choosing is not a fiction, regardless of how the brain works. It is a real neural process, with the obvious function of selecting behavior according to its foreseeable consequences. It responds to information from the senses, including the warnings of other people. You cannot step outside it or let it go on without you, because it is you.

POINTS TO PONDER

• Science is guaranteed to chip away at the concept of Free Will, because the scientific mode of explanation cannot accommodate the mysterious notion of *uncaused causation* that underlies the will.

• Everything we do is an evolutionary adaptation designed to carry out a major function. The illusion of Free Will falls into this category.

• New imaging techniques have tied every thought and emotion to neural activity.

• If scientists wanted to show that people had Free Will, what would they look for? Some random neural event that the rest of the brain amplifies into a signal triggering behavior? But a random event does not fit the concept of Free Will any more than a lawful one does.

• Causal explanations for behavior, both biological and environmental, *do not corrode responsibility*.

MORE TO EXPLORE

• The excerpts were adapted from Steven Pinker's book, *The Blank Slate,* Chapter 10. To learn more, read the chapter, "The Fear of Determinism."

• Pinker's books are original works of evolutionary psychology. Check out his other bestsellers: *The Language Instinct* and *How the Mind Works.*

The Astonishing Hypothesis

by V. S. Ramachandran

Vilayanur Ramachandran is a neuroscientist and Director, Center for Brain and Cognition, University of California, San Diego.

*W*hat Francis Crick referred to as "the astonishing hypothesis" is the notion that our conscious experience and sense of self is based entirely on the activity of a hundred billion bits of jelly, the neurons that constitute the brain. We take this for granted in these enlightened times, but even so it never ceases to amaze me.

Some scholars have criticized Crick's tongue-in-cheek phrase (and title of his book) on the grounds that the hypothesis he refers to is "neither astonishing nor a hypothesis." (Since we already know it to be true.) Yet the far reaching philosophical, moral and ethical dilemmas posed by his hypothesis have not been recognized widely enough. It is in many ways the ultimate dangerous idea.

Let's put this in historical perspective. Freud once pointed out that the history of ideas in the last few centuries has been punctuated by "revolutions" major upheavals of thought that have forever altered

"*You*, your joys and your sorrows,
your memories and your ambitions,
your sense of personal identity and
Free Will, are in fact no more than
the behavior of a vast assembly of
nerve cells and their associated
molecules. As Lewis Carroll's Alice
might have said: 'You're nothing
but a pack of neurons.'"

—**Francis Crick, Ph.D.**

our view of ourselves and our place in the cosmos.

First, there was the Copernican system dethroning the earth as the center of the cosmos.

Second, was the Darwinian revolution; the idea that far from being the climax of *intelligent design* we are merely neotonous apes that happen to be slightly cleverer than our cousins.

Third, the Freudian view that even though you claim to be "in charge" of your life, your behavior is in fact governed by a cauldron of drives and motives of which you are largely unconscious.

Fourth, the discovery of DNA and the genetic code with its implication (to quote James Watson) that "There are only molecules. Everything else is sociology."

To this list we can now add the fifth, the "neuroscience revolution" and its corollary pointed out by Crick—the "astonishing hypothesis"—that even our loftiest thoughts and aspirations are mere by products of neural activity. We are nothing but a pack of neurons. If all this seems dehumanizing, you haven't seen anything yet.

POINTS TO PONDER

• We are all merely reflections in a hall of mirrors of a single cosmic reality.

• The human brain, it has been said, is the most complexly organized structure in the universe and to appreciate this you have to look at some numbers. The brain is made up of one-hundred billion nerve cells or "neurons" which form the basic structure and functional units of the nervous system. Each neuron makes something like one thousand to ten thousand contacts with other neurons and these points of contact are called synapses.

TO GO DEEPER

Read Ramachandran's book: *A Brief Tour of Human Consciousness.* You will gain insights into the mind on such everyday human experiences as pain, sight, and the appreciation of beauty.

*The very notion of a separate
"you" or "I" is an illusion, like the
passage of time itself.*

It's an Ancient Artifact

by Sam Harris

Sam Harris is a graduate in philosophy from Stanford University. For 20 years, he has studied Eastern and Western religious traditions. He is now completing his doctorate in neuroscience.

𝓕ree Will is an illusion in that it cannot even be rendered coherent *conceptually*, since no one has ever described a manner in which mental and physical events could arise that would attest to its existence. Surely, most illusions are made of sterner stuff than this. If, for instance, a man believes that his dental fillings are receiving radio broadcasts, or that his sister has been replaced by an alien who looks exactly like her, we have no difficulty specifying what would have to be true of the world for his beliefs to be true. Strangely, our notion of Free Will achieves no such intelligibility. As a concept, it simply has no descriptive or logical moorings.

The belief that human beings are endowed with Free Will underwrites both our religious conception of "sin" and our judicial ideal of "retributive justice." Without Free Will, sinners would just be poorly calibrated clockwork, and any notion of justice that emphasized their punishment (rather than rehabilitation or mere containment) would seem deeply incongruous. Happily, we will find that we need no illusions about a person's place in the causal order to hold him accountable for his actions. We can find secure foundations for ethics and the rule of law without succumbing to illusions.

The idea of Free Will is an ancient artifact of philosophy as well as a subject of occasional, if guilty, interest among scientists. Despite the clever exertions of many philosophers who have sought to render Free Will "compatible" with deterministic accounts of mind and brain, the project seems hopeless. The endurance of Free Will, as a problem in need of analysis, is attributable to the fact that most of us feel that we freely author our own actions (however difficult it may be to make sense of this notion in logical or scientific terms).

What most people overlook is that the concept of Free Will does not correspond to any subjective fact about us. Consequently, even rigorous introspection soon grows as hostile to the idea of Free Will as the equations of physics have, because apparent acts of volition merely arise, spontaneously and cannot be traced to point of origin in the stream of consciousness.

POINTS TO PONDER

• A moment or two of self-scrutiny and the reader might observe than he no more authors the next thought he thinks than the next thought I write.

• Iron Age beliefs—about God, the soul, sin, and Free Will—continue to impede medical research and distort public policy.

TO GO DEEPER

• Read Sam Harris's books, *The End of Faith: Religion, Terror, and the Future of Reason* and *Letters to a Christian Nation.*

• Visit his website at www.samharris.org.

Free Will's Last Stand

by Clay Shirky

Clay Shirky is a Social & Technology Network Topology Researcher; Adjunct Professor, NYU Graduate School of Interactive Telecommunications Program.

Free Will is going away. It's time to redesign society to take that into account.

In 2002, a group of teenagers sued McDonald's for making them fat. They claimed that the corporation used promotional techniques to get them to eat more than they should. The suit was condemned as an the erosion of the sense of Free Will and personal responsibility in our society. Less widely remarked upon was that the teenagers were offering an accurate account of human behavior.

Consider the phenomenon of *super-sizing*, where a restaurant patron is offered the chance to increase the portion size of their meal for some small amount of money. This presents a problem for the *concept* of Free Will. The patron has already made a calculation about the amount of money they are willing to pay in return for a particular amount of food.

However, when the question is re-asked—not "Would you pay $5.79 for this total amount of food?" but "Would you pay an additional 30 cents for more French fries?"—patrons often say yes, despite having answered "No" moments before to an economically identical question.

Super-sizing is designed to subvert conscious judgment, and it works. By re-framing the question, fast food companies have found ways to take advantages of weaknesses in our analytical apparatus, weaknesses that are being documented daily in behavioral economics and evolutionary psychology.

This matters for more than just fat teenagers. Our legal, political, and economic systems all assume that people are uniformly capable of consciously retraining their behaviors. As a result, we regard decisions they make as being valid and hold them responsible for actions they take, as in contract law or criminal trials. Then, in order to get around the fact that some people obviously aren't capable of controlling their behavior, we carve out exemptions. In U.S. criminal law, a 15 year old who commits a crime is treated differently than a 16 year old. A crime committed in the heat of the moment is treated specially. Some actions are not crimes because their perpetrator is judged mentally incapable, whether through developmental disabilities or other forms of legally defined insanity.

This theoretical divide, between the mass of people with a uniform amount of Free Will and a small set of exceptional individuals, has been broadly stable for centuries, in part because it was based on ignorance. As long as we were unable to locate any biological source of Free Will, treating the mass of people as if each of them had the same degree of control over their lives made perfect sense. However, today that notion of Free Will is being eroded as our understanding of the biological causes of behavior improves.

Criminal law is just one area where our concept of Free Will is eroding:

- We know that men make more aggressive decisions after they have been shown pictures of attractive female faces.
- We know women are more likely to commit infidelity on days they are fertile.
- We know that patients committing involuntary physical actions routinely (and incorrectly) report that they decided to undertake those actions to preserve their feeling of control.

• We know people will drive across town to save $10 on a $50 appliance, but not on a $25,000 car.
• We know that the design of the ballot affects a voter's choices.

In the coming decades, our concept of Free Will, based as it is now on ignorance of its actual mechanisms, will be destroyed by what we learn about the actual workings of the brain.

We can wait for that collision, and decide what to do then, or we can begin thinking through what sort of legal, political, and economic systems we need in a world where our old concept of Free Will is rendered inoperable.

TO GO DEEPER
• Clay Shirky's essay is featured in John Brockman's book, *What Is Your Dangerous Idea? Today's Leading Thinkers on the Unthinkable,* and on Edge.org, a website teeming with mind-bending essays by prominent thinkers. Edge Foundation, Inc., was established in 1988 as an outgrowth of a group known as The Reality Club.
• Visit his website: www.shirky.com.

A Mouse Tale

by Tamler Sommers

Tamler Sommers is Assistant Professor of Philosophy at the University of Minnesota, Morris. He received his Ph.D. at Duke University.

*I*magine for a moment that instead of Timothy McVeigh destroying the Murrah Federal Building in Oklahoma City, it had been a mouse. Suppose this mouse got into the wiring of the electrical system, tangled the circuits and caused a big fire, killing all those inside. Now think of the victims' families.

There would, of course, still be enormous grief and suffering, but there would be one significant difference: There would no resentment, no consuming anger, no hatred, no need to see the perpetrator punished (even if the mouse somehow got out of the building) in order to experience "closure." Why the difference? Because McVeigh, we think, committed this terrible act out of his own Free Will. He chose to do it, and he could have chosen not to. McVeigh, then, is morally responsible for the death of the victims in a way that the mouse would not be. And our sense of justice demands that he pay for this crime.

There is an undeniable human tendency to see ourselves as free and morally responsible beings. But there's a problem. We also believe—most of us anyhow—that our environment and our heredity entirely shape our characters. (What else could?) But we aren't responsible for our environment, and we aren't responsible for our heredity. So we aren't responsible for our characters. But then how can we be responsible for acts that arise from our characters? There's a simple but extremely unpopular answer to this question: *We aren't.*

We are not and cannot be ultimately responsible for our behavior. According to this argument, while it may be of great pragmatic value to hold people responsible for their actions, and to employ systems of reward and punishment, no one is really deserving of blame or praise for anything.

TO GO DEEPER

Visit Tamler's website (www.morris.umn.edu/academic/philosophy/Sommers/tamlersommers.htm) for two wonderful articles on Free Will. Click on "On-Line Publications," then read "The Illusion of Freedom Evolves" and "Interview with Galen Strawson."

What is Naturalism?

by Thomas W. Clark

Tom Clark is the founder and director of the Center for Naturalism, based in Somerville, MA.

"*N*aturalism" is a philosophical viewpoint that says there is a single, natural world, not split into the natural and supernatural, and we are completely included in that world. There is nothing supernatural about us. Naturalism is based on taking science—not faith, revelation, intuition or tradition—as our way of deciding what ultimately exists. One way to understand it is to pose a basic question: How do we explain human behavior? There are two standard explanations:

1. The "Free Will" Explanation
This one involves the traditional view that people, although they may be influenced in many respects, choose their behavior using what philosophers call "contra-causal" Free Will, a will which is itself not fully determined by anything else. This sort of Free Will is often thought to be exercised by a non-physical soul or consciousness that's independent of

45

causality. On this view, persons are in some respect first causes, agents who cause but are not fully caused themselves. To explain behavior we appeal, ultimately, to contra-causal Free Will, even though we admit there are various causes and factors that influence people's character, motives, impulses, and decisions.

2. The Scientific Explanation

Science finds no evidence for the existence of the non-physical soul or contra-causal Free Will, and instead looks at all the factors coming together in a certain moment, taking the genetics and history of the person into account. It explains why the person is the way she is, and then explains behavior in terms of how that person interacts with their current environment. If we replayed the tape of history, with all factors exactly the same, inside and outside the person, the same behavior would have arisen.

The first explanation involves something supernatural, namely the freely-willing soul. The second, since it's based in science, is entirely naturalistic. Naturalism denies the existence of gods, ghosts, angels, or non-physical entities that can't be confirmed to exist or be explained by its methods. And it denies we have souls that have contra-causal Free Will, defined as the capacity to cause things without itself being fully caused in turn. Having this sort of Free Will is to be privileged over nature. It's to be little gods, with a special power over the world: to be in some important sense self-created, so that we get to take ultimate credit and blame for who we are and what we do.

Naturalism, the view that we are not little gods, but fully natural, fully caused creatures, who don't have Free Will, is empowering, both personally and socially. It can give us power, because it doesn't shrink from the insight that people are fully caused creatures. Seeing the causal story behind the self and its choices gives us power to control the circumstances that inspire creativity and help realize our goals.

But there's a catch: the you (that's getting all this power) is reconceptualized as a fully caused function of the world surrounding it, not as a first cause. So you don't get to take ultimate credit and blame, to be as egoistical, as prideful, or as blaming, or as retributive. Instead, we're led to be more understanding and empathetic, since we'll see that *there but for circumstances go I.*

MORE TO EXPLORE

• *The Center for Naturalism* is devoted to increasing public awareness of scientific Naturalism and its implications for social and personal well-being. By means of lectures, publications and research, the CFN seeks to foster the understanding that human beings are entirely natural phenomena, and that human flourishing is best achieved in the light of such understanding.

• Visit Naturalism's websites at naturalism.org and centerfornaturalism.org.

Living Happily & Morally

by Susan Blackmore

Sue Blackmore is Senior Lecturer in Psychology at the University of the West of England, Bristol. She has a degree in psychology and physiology from Oxford University.

*I*t is possible to live happily and morally without believing in Free Will. As Samuel Johnson said: "All theory is against the freedom of the will, and all experience is for it."

With recent developments in neuroscience and theories of consciousness, theory is even more against it than it was in his time, more than 200 years ago. So I long ago set about systematically changing the experience. I now have no feeling of acting with Free Will, although the feeling took many years to ebb away.

But what happens?

People say I'm lying! They say it's impossible and so I must be deluding myself to preserve my theory. And what can I do or say to challenge them? I have no idea—other than to suggest that other people try the exercise, demanding as it is.

Photo of Susan Blackmore by Jayne Russell

When the feeling is gone, decisions just happen with no sense of anyone making them, but then a new question arises—will the decisions be morally acceptable? Here, I have made a great leap of faith: It seems that when people throw out the illusion of an inner self who acts, as many mystics and Buddhist practitioners have done, they generally do behave in ways that we think of as moral or good. So perhaps giving up Free Will is not as dangerous as it sounds.

As for giving up the sense of an inner conscious self altogether—this is very much harder. I just keep on seeming to exist. But though I cannot prove it— I think it is true that I don't.

TO GO DEEPER
• Read Sue Blackmore's latest book: *Conversations on Consciousness: What the Best Minds Think about the Brain, Free Will, and What It Means to Be Human,* Oxford University Press, 2006.
• Visit her website: *www.susanblackmore.co.uk*
• Peruse her other books: *The Meme Machine* and *Consciousness: An Introduction.*

Quotable Quotes

*The contemporary person stands
in a strange position: the old
has fallen away, and it was a deception,
and the new has not yet arrived.*

—OSHO

"Deeds are done, events happen,
and there is no individual doer thereof."

—Buddha

"Actions do exist, and also their
consequences, but the person who acts
does not exist."

—Buddha

"Once one's physiology has become integrated enough to see everything 'under the gaze of eternity' —that is, once one has become *enlightened*—one recognizes that Free Will is only an illusion produced by one's prior inadequate perceptual and conceptual perspective: in *Upanishadic* terms, a product of *maya*."

—Baruch Spinoza, *philosopher*

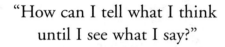

"How can I tell what I think
until I see what I say?"

—E. M. Forster, *A Room with a View*

"Give me the choice between my actions being strict *causal outcomes* of my genes, my history, my personality, the state of my mind/brain, and the current environment, and I will take that, every day of the week, over the view that when I deliberate or act, I do so randomly, because my will has flown the causal coop."

—Owen Flanagan, *The Problem of the Soul*

"Free Will is doing gladly and freely
what one must do."

—**Carl Jung,** *psychiatrist*

"We are mere machines. And machines may
not boast, nor feel proud of their performance, nor
claim personal merit for it."

—**Mark Twain,** *What is Man?*

"Our behavior is not random, so it must have a *cause*. And if behavior has a cause, it must not be free.

—**Matt Ridley,** *Nature Via Nurture*

"I do not believe in Free Will. Schopenhauer's words, *Man can do what he wants, but he cannot will what he wants*, accompany me in all situations throughout my life and reconcile me with the actions of others, even if they are rather painful to me. This awareness of the lack of Free Will keeps me from taking myself and my fellow men too seriously as acting and deciding individuals, and from losing my temper."

—**Albert Einstein,** *My Credo*

"The first dogma which I came to disbelieve was that of Free Will. It seemed to me that all notions of matter were *determined* by the laws of physics and could not be influenced by human wills."
—**Bertrand Russell,** *philosopher*

"The universe is a gigantic clockwork mechanism, slavishly unfolding according to deterministic laws. How then does a free agent act? There is simply no room in this *causally closed system* for an immaterial mind to bend the paths of atoms without coming into contact with physical laws. Nor does the famed indeterminacy of quantum mechanics help minds to gain purchase on the material world."
—**Paul Davies,** *The Mind of God*

"The mind is *determined* to wish for this or that by a *cause*, which has also been determined by another cause, and this again by another, and so on to infinity. This realization teaches us to hate no one, to despise no one, to mock no one, to be angry with no one, and to envy no one."

—**Baruch Spinoza,** *philosopher*

Byron Katie

"Are you breathing yourself? No? Well, maybe you're not thinking yourself or making decisions either. Maybe it (you) doesn't move until it moves, like a breath, like the wind. Are you telling yourself the story of how you are doing it to keep from the awareness that you are nature and are flowing perfectly?"

—Byron Katie, *Loving What Is*

Visit Katie's website at www.thework.org.

"Do you think I know what I am doing, that for one breath or half-breath I belong to myself, as much as a pen knows what it is writing or a ball can guess where it is going."

—**Rumi,** *poet*

"*Hume's Fork:* Either our actions are determined, in which case we are not responsible for them, or they are the result of random events, in which case we are not responsible for them."

—*Oxford Dictionary of Philosophy*

"I'm concerned with what's true. For me, the evolution/creation war is really just a battle. It's a skirmish in a larger war between supernaturalism and naturalism."

—Richard Dawkins, *The God Delusion*

"Perhaps the idea of will power or Free Will is a cultural phenomenon. If so, we must not assign blame to people for personal failures, we should instead understand the larger system and its influence on the individual."

—Heidi Ravven, *philosopher*

"When man studies himself with honest impartiality, he observes that he is not the voluntary artisan of his feelings or of his thoughts, and that his feelings and his thoughts are only phenomena which happen to him."

—Hubert Benoit, *Zen and the Psychology of Transformation*

"The mind-body problem splits the mind to one side and the body and its brain to the other. This view is no longer mainstream in science or philosophy, although it is probably the view that most humans today regard as their own."

—**Antonio Damasio,** *Looking for Spinoza*

"Neuroscience brooks no distinction between me and the physical processes of my brain. It rejects the notion of a freely-willed act, because I have no 'will' above and beyond the neurochemical reactions that make me tick."

—**Kathryn Schultz,** *The Nation* (1-9-2006)

"If I hadn't spent so much time studying Earthlings," said the Tralfamadorian, "I wouldn't have any idea what was meant by Free Will. I've visited thirty-one inhabited planets in the universe, and I have studied reports on one hundred more. Only on Earth is there any talk of Free Will."

—**Kurt Vonnegut,** *Slaughterhouse Five*

"The man who said 'I'd rather be lucky than good' saw deeply into life. People are afraid to face how great a part of life is dependent on luck. It's scary to think so much is out of one's control."

—Woody Allen, *Matchpoint*

"The next state of the physical universe is always *determined* by the previous state. And given a certain brain-state plus an environment, you could never have acted otherwise."

—Thomas Metzinger, *Being No One*

"When a man acts in ways that annoy us we wish to think him wicked, and we refuse to face the fact that his annoying behavior is the result of antecedent *causes* which, if you follow them long enough, will take you beyond the moment of his birth, and therefore to events for which he cannot be held responsible by any stretch of imagination. When a motorcar fails to start, we do not attribute its annoying behavior to sin, we do not say, you are a wicked motorcar, and you shall not have any more gasoline until you go."

—**Bertrand Russell,** *philosopher*

"It is tempting to believe that our minds float free of our genomes. But such beliefs are completely at odds with everything that scientists have learned in molecular biology in the past decade."

—Gary Marcus, *The Birth of the Mind*

"I've yet to discover a single interpretation of *genetic determinism* that carries any of the implications people seem to worry so much about. On the contrary, it turns out that whatever applies to genes applies equally to environments. So if people fear genetic determinism, they should be worrying equally about *environmental determinism*."

—Helena Cronin, *philosopher*

"I am convinced that we must commit ourselves to the view that a universal ethics is possible, and that we ought to seek to understand it and define it. It is a staggering idea, and one that on casual thought seems preposterous. Yet there is no way out."

—Michael S. Gazzaniga, *The Ethical Brain*

"I am a brain, my dear Watson, and the rest of me is a mere appendage."

— **Sherlock Holmes**

"There is no such thing as Free Will. The mind is induced to wish this or that by some cause, and that cause is determined by another cause, and so on back to infinity."

—**Baruch Spinoza,** *philosopher*

"We are importantly unpredictable except for our *general tendencies and patterns*. We will go to sleep at night, get up in the morning, tend to hug our spouse at least three or four times a day, but exactly when, or what words will come out of our mouths, that's unpredictable. So we mustn't fear the story science seems to tell, that we are just robots."

—Patricia Churchland, UCSD *professor*

"Cause and effect, means and ends, seed and fruit cannot be severed; for the effect already blooms in the cause, the end preexists in the means, the fruit in the seed."

—Ralph Waldo Emerson

"The mind is what the brain does, and so every mental event, from falling in love to worrying about our taxes, is going to show up as a brain event. In fact, if one were to find an aspect of thought that did not correspond to a brain event, it would be the discovery of the century."

—Paul Bloom, *Descartes' Baby*

Glossary

CAUSALITY, CAUSAL, CAUSED Humans act the way they do because of the various causes that shape them, whether these be genetic or environmental. We do not have the capacity to act outside of the causal connections that link us in every respect to the rest of the world.

• **Contra-causal:** *Contra* means "against." Contra-causal means against causality or the laws of cause-and-effect. Free Will is a contra-causal belief.

CHAOS THEORY The behavior of certain non-linear dynamical systems (such as the brain) exhibits a phenomenon known as chaos. Among the characteristics of chaotic systems is sensitivity to initial conditions (the butterfly effect). As a result of this sensitivity, the behavior of systems that exhibit chaos appears to be random, even though the system is deterministic.

CONDITIONING Environmental input. Our conditioning includes what we learn from our parents, schooling, culture, social status, and historical time-slot. Our experiences.

DECISION-MAKING The cognitive process leading to the selection of a course of action among alternatives. The anterior cingulate cortex and orbitofrontal cortex are brain regions involved in decision-making.

DETERMINISM The view that every event, without exception, is causally determined by prior events. Human thoughts and actions are events. Therefore, human thoughts and actions are, without exception, causally determined by prior events.

DUALISM The term 'dualism' has a variety of uses in the history of thought. In general, the idea is that, for some particular domain, there are two kinds of things. In the philosophy of mind, dualism is the theory that the mental and the physical—or the mind and body or mind and brain—are two different kinds of things: supernatural and natural. The myth of Free Will is an example of dualism.

• **Cartesian Dualism:** René Descartes (1641) said that the mind is a nonphysical substance. Descartes was the first to clearly identify the mind with consciousness and self-awareness and to distinguish this from the brain.

EXISTENTIALISTS People who accept that while no meaning has been designed into the universe, we can each creatively provide meaning for ourselves. Author Susan Blackmore says, "We humans can, and do, make up our own purposes, but ultimately the universe has none. All the wonderfully complex and beautifully designed things we see around us were built by the same purposeless process—evolution by natural selection."

FATALISM The belief that all events are predetermined and therefore inevitable, that something will happen no matter what we do. A submissive attitude to events. By contrast, *determinism* leaves "us" in the picture, so that what we know matters.

FREE WILL The view that humans have a "self" or "spirit" or "soul" or "some magical quality" that controls the brain's decision-making circuitry. This airy, celestial, dreamlike, ghostly, impalpable, and shadowy agent can—if and when it feels like it—deftly override our genes and conditioning, so that we may act randomly. The doctrine of Free Will denies the laws of cause-and-effect (nature) and makes them irrelevant. It states that humans are originators or first causes.

THE GHOST IN THE MACHINE   A derogatory phrase that refers to the presence of a "self," "spirit," or "soul" that directs the brain. British philosopher Gilbert Ryle's description for Rene Descartes' mind-body dualism: Mental activity is of a different category from physical activity.

INDETERMINISM The stance that *not* all events are wholly determined by prior causes, that humans have Free Will and can be first causes.

NATURALISM A worldview that says nature is all there is and nothing supernatural exists. Go to *The Center for Naturalism* for an introduction to this timely philosophy: www.centerfornaturalism.org.

NEUROSCIENCE   Any of the sciences, such as neurochemistry and experimental psychology, that deal with the structure or function of the nervous system and brain.
• **Neurons:** Nerve cells in the brain specialized for the transmission of information. It comprises a cell body, an axon (for electrical output signals), and dendrites (to receive incoming electrical signals).
• **Mirror Neurons:** Nerve cells in the brain specialized for empathy, learning, and imitation.

Acknowledgments

First, I would like to thank Ramesh S. Balsekar for making the illusion of Free Will the main topic of his books and talks. People from all over the world "get it" because he teaches the principles of non-doership so clearly, lovingly, and humorously.

Ramesh, you taught me that believing in fantasies, like Free Will, causes more harm than good and that dropping them can lead to a kinder, more compassionate world.

Without the books, research, and wisdom of Susan Blackmore, Thomas Clark, Michael Shermer, Daniel M. Wegner, William B. Provine, Laurence Tancredi, Steven Pinker, Sam Harris, Daniel C. Dennett, V. S. Ramachandran, Clay Shirky, Tamler Sommers, and Lee M. Silver, this anthology would not exist. Many thanks for giving me permission to share your wonderful words.

I would also like to express my gratitude to Byron Katie, author of *Loving What Is*, for living joyously without acting "as if" she's the doer.

References

Adams, Scott. *God's Debris: A Thought Experiment.* New York: Andrews McMeel, 2001.

Balsekar, Ramesh. *Peace and Harmony in Daily Living.* Mumbai: Yogi Impressions, 2003.

Berthoz, Alain. *Emotion & Reason.* Oxford University Press, 2003. Page 65.

Blackmore, Susan. *What We Believe but Cannot Prove.* NY: Harper, 2006. Pages 40-41. *Conversations on Consciousness.* Oxford University Press, 2006. Page 63.

Bloom, Paul. *Descartes Baby.* New York: Basic Books, 2004. Quote from *Seed* magazine, June-July 2006. Page 20.

Clark, Thomas. www.centerfornaturalism.org and www.naturalism.org.

Dawkins, Richard. *The God Delusion.* New York: Houghton Mifflin Company, 2006.

Dennett, Daniel C. *Freedom Evolves.* New York: Penguin Putnam, 2003. Pages 1, 10, 13.

Dowret, Arnell. Onewitheverything.org. Tenet 3. "Human behavior is the result of causes."

Flanagan, Owen. *The Problem of the Soul.* New York: Perseus Books, 2002. Page 128.

Gazzaniga, Michael S. *The Ethical Brain.* New York: Dana Press, 2005. Pages 102, 178.

Harris, Sam. 2005. *The End of Faith.* New York: W. W. Norton. Pages 272-274.

Marcus, Gary. *The Birth of the Mind.* New York:
Basic Books, 2004. Page 86.

Osho. *Zen: It's History and Teachings.* UK: The
Bridgewater Book Co., 2004. Page 137.

Pinker, Steven. *The Blank Slate.* New York:
Penguin Books, 2002. Pages 174-5,184-5.

Provine, William B. "The Myth of Free Will and
Its Evil Consequences." Lecture to the
Santa Fe Institute on March 20, 2003.

Ramachandran, V. S. From John Brockman's book,
What Is Your Dangerous Idea? New York:
Harper Perennial, 2007.

Shermer, Michael. From John Brockman's book,
What We Believe but Cannot Prove. New
York: Harper Perennial, 2006. Pages 38-39.

Shirky, Clay. From John Brockman's book, *What Is
Your Dangerous Idea?* NY: Harper, 2007.

Silver, Lee M. *Challenging Nature: The Clash of
Science and Spirituality at the New Frontiers
of Life.* New York: HarperCollins, 2006.
Pages 58-61, 64.

Sommers, Tamler. *The Believer* magazine; March
2003. www.believermag.com

Tancredi, Laurence. *Hardwired Behavior.*
Cambridge University Press, 2005. Adapted
from pages 74-75.

Wegner, Daniel M. *The Illusion of Conscious Will.*
Cambridge: MIT Press, 2002. Adapted
from pages 1-2, 341-342.

Quick Order Form

You may order books from Amazon.com or by using the simple form below. Send your order to:

Café Essays
PMB 300
P. O. Box 223300
Princeville, HI 96722

Name: _____

Address: _____

City: _____

State & Zip Code:_____

Email Address: _____

Book Price: $10 US / $12 Canada
Book Price for 3 or more: $8 US / $10 Canada
Add $2 to the price of each book for shipping.
Payment: Cash or Check
Make check payable to "Cris Evatt."

HOT OFF THE PRESS!

Why do we choose chocolate ice cream over vanilla? Why do we select one lover over another?

"A fascinating introduction to an important new area."
—*Steven Pinker*

Why Choose This Book?

How We Make Decisions

Read Montague

Neuroscientist Read Montague deftly marries psychology and neuroscience as he probes how we make choices.

Notes

Notes

Notes

Notes

Notes